The Fantastic Book of
BOARD GAMES

ST. MARTIN'S PRESS · NEW YORK

Library of Congress Cataloging-in-Publication Data
Great games book.
The fantastic book of board games /by A & C Black Ltd. − 1st U.S. ed.
p. cm.
Originally published under title: The Great games book. 1985.
1. Board games.   I. A & C Black Ltd.   II. Title.

GV1312.G74   1988   794.2—dc19   88-739
ISBN 0-312-02049-X

First published in Great Britain by A & C Black (Publishers) Ltd.,
under the title *The Great Games Book*.

First U.S. Edition, 1988

10   9   8   7   6   5   4   3   2   1

Cover design by Raquel Jaramillo
Front cover illustration by Fulvio Testa
Color separations by Positive Colour Ltd., Maldon
Printed in Italy by Arnoldo Mondadori, Verona

THE GAMES

In order of appearance

ROOT the

Midnight:
Three faithful ferrets keep watch over the scouts' supply tents but deep beneath them **Operation Scout About** is underway.

ROOT THE LOOT
A game for two players. One commands three moles on a midnight raid while the other controls three ferrets who are guarding the loot.

MOLES
Your objective is to pick up as much loot as possible and return it to the safety of H.Q. without being caught by the ferrets. Each time you land in a tent section, shout 'Root the Loot', then add the loot score to the running total for that mole. You may return to the same loot as often as you like before returning to H.Q. Be sure to conceal your running totals from the ferrets. Remember you are specially trained kamikazi raiders and will do anything, even sacrifice yourself and your loot, to help a comrade with a higher running total escape the ferrets and get back to H.Q. The final raid score is your only concern.

FERRETS
Your objective is to capture all the moles as quickly as possible before too much loot is lost. To capture a mole, simply land on the same space, either on the surface or underground. The mole then forfeits any score he is carrying and is removed from the board.

LOOT

SCOUT ABOUT

10

5 5

CLAPHAM JUNCTION

MOVES

Moves on the surface are from one tent section to another or to and from adjacent guy rope areas. Underground, one move is from one tunnel junction to another. Moles are faster than ferrets and must always move two spaces. This can include one space forward and one space back if desired. As long as one mole turn follows one ferret turn, any one of the opposing teams may make a move. One mole may be out rooting whilst two wait in H.Q. for a good opportunity to emerge. Similarly ferrets may find it advantageous as a team to have two on guard whilst one chases. Ferrets may never enter the moles' H.Q.

YOU WILL NEED

3 ferret counters, 3 mole counters, paper and pencil. Mark each mole counter A, B, and C so it is clear when keeping running totals which mole is carrying what score.

TO BEGIN

Place one ferret in any section of each tent and the moles anywhere in H.Q. Moles can then begin their raid. The first raid ends when all moles have been captured. When all moles have been lost make a grand total of their safe loot scores and enter it on the **Grand Score Card** under **Raid One**. Players then swap roles. The ferret player takes over the moles to play **Raid Two** and tries to beat the **Raid One** score to win.

Devised and illustrated by Jez Alborough

GRAND TOTALS

RAID ONE.......

RAID TWO.......

WE SALUTE YOU COMRADES

YOU ARE HERE

LUDO PARK

Illustrated by Angela Barrett

THIS WAY

HOME

This way

How to Play

For two to four players.
Each player places four counters of one colour in his/her quarter of the garden. The highest score on the throw of a dice decides who will start the game.

Each player starts on a square marked 'This way' and travels in the direction indicated until he/she reaches the square before that from which he/she started and then along the coloured row to 'Home'.

Players may enter or advance any one of their counters at each turn. Players throw the dice once each turn unless a six is thrown which allows them another throw. Different counters may be moved each time.

Whenever a counter lands on a space already taken by an opponent, the occupier must be put back in his/her quarter. If a counter lands on a square occupied by one of the same colour it is placed on top of it. All counters of one colour may rest in one square.

The player whose four counters are 'Home' first is the winner.

The Amazing ➤ J. SLINGSBY GREBE G

DEVISED BY QUENTIN BLAKE AND JOHN YEOMAN with the personal consultation of

J. SLINGSBY GREBE ~BOY GENIUS!

START HERE

JSG rescuing the life boat "Saucy Washerwoman" in stormy seas after it had hit a rock off Land's End.

J. Slingsby Grebe — Boy Genius — is the most astonishing figure of our time. He is already holder of many awards, cups and medals. He holds the Natural History Medal of the Photographic Society and the Photographic Medal of the Natural History Society. He has the Gold Medal of the Life Boat Institute for saving a life boat off Land's End. He has recently been awarded the Albert Einstein Prize for Pinball Wizardry and won the Isle of Man T.T. Trophy (Motorised Bedsteads class) for the fourth year running.

JSG demonstrating Grebe's Nudge as his score approaches 1,897,983,496,812 in the Pinball Wizardry Finals at Hastings.

ACTUAL SIZE

UTTER BRILLIANCE for JSG

The Medal

JSG in a winning position in the last lap of the Isle of Man T.T. Trophy (Motorised Bedsteads class).

A marble bust of JSG (carved by himself).

TESTED AND JSG GUARANTEED

RULES OF THE GAME

1: Any number of potential geniuses can play.
2: Use one dice.
3: Each player throws in turn.
4: The utterly brilliant winner is the first to reach the final gold medallist's square exactly.

1 2 3 4 5

6 *Disguised a... theft of Cr... spaces.*

36 35 34

33 *You perform Beethoven's triple concerto for violin, bassoon and mouthorgan single-handed. Go forward 5 spaces.*

37 *Over-exertion causes bad attack of striped fever. Go back 3 spaces.*

38

39

40

42 43

41 *With gentle persuasion you succeed in taming the Beast from Planet X. Have another turn.*

76 75

73 72 71

74 *Mice in your bagpipes ruin your chances in the Highland Games decathlon. Go back 2 spaces.*

70 *Slight error destr... hopes of discove... formula for inter... fuel, and your pa... Miss a turn.*

77 *Using your own design of oxygen cylinder and weighted shoes, you break the World Underwater Disco Dancing Endurance Record. Go forward 4 spaces.*

78

79

80

81

Also a few deadly tarantulas

83 84 85 86

82 *You frustrate the plans of mad Professor Grosswurtz to swamp the Northern Hemisphere with David Essex clones produced in his secret laboratory. Go forward 3 spaces.*

87 *Giant python escapes on the return of your Zoo Quest to South America. Go back 3 spaces.*

7 8 9

10 Slightly indisposed after demonstrating your cordon bleu recipe for frog in tomato sauce. Go back 2 spaces.

11 12 13

14 Wearing your specially designed crampons you rescue seven distressed kittens and one fireman from a tree. Go forward 4 spaces.

15 16

17 Through over-excitement you take this corner badly and skid off the page. Miss a turn.

18

19

20

21 Using your patented skateboard you help 376 old ladies to cross the road in four hours. Go forward 5 spaces.

...foil attempted ...orward 3

31 30 29

27 26

24 23 22

28 Eleventh hour rescue of kidnapped society beauty from railway line earns you a free British Rail runaround ticket. Go forward 3 spaces.

25 Toe gets stuck in bath-tap while you plan your next undertaking. Miss a turn.

47 48

50 51 52

54 55

56 A Dictionary falls on your head while you are translating the works of Shakespeare into Swahili. Go back 2 spaces.

46 Incapacitated through Nicodemus Grudge sewing up the arms and legs of your clothes. Go back 2 spaces.

49 Incorrect fitting of rocket-powered roller skates puts you into reverse. Go back 5 spaces.

53 Carrying the mayor and aldermen of Liverpool on your shoulders, you become the first person to cross the Mersey on a tightrope. Go forward 3 spaces.

57

58

59

69 68 67

65 64 63

62 61

66 You totally subdue rampaging bull in Harrods' china department, using eye-to-eye contact alone. Go forward 5 spaces.

60 Your performance in the leading role of ''Hamlet on Ice'' ruined by a heatwave. Go back 3 spaces.

89 90 91

93 94

96 97 98 99 100

92 Giant computer collapses after you beat it in mental arithmetic test. Go forward 4 spaces.

95 Your hopes of establishing hang-gliding record over London dashed after unfortunate encounter with Lord Nelson. Go back 4 spaces.

AIEEEEEE!!

Ingredients

2 players	25 squares of paper
4 counters (pigs)	1 lb cooked pork sausages

How to Play

The object of the game is to be first to reach the pig in the centre of the pantry. The game has two elements: the *playing board,* left, and the *scoring card,* below. Each player has a playing pig and a scoring pig. Place the playing pigs on the No. 1 squares of the *playing board.* Toss a coin to start. Loser, Player A, goes first by placing his scoring pig to point either across or down one of the rows of numbers on the *scoring card.* He scores nothing.

Player B now places his scoring pig to point along a row of numbers at right angles to Player A's row. The *direction* each player's scoring pig is pointing remains fixed throughout the game. Player B now advances his/her playing pig by the number in the square where A's and B's rows meet on the *scoring card.* Cover that number to take it out of the game.

Player B's scoring pig now remains where it is while Player A moves his/her pig to a row which points to a desired score. And so on. Whenever you land on a handsome-piggy blue square at each corner of the course, you double your next score. The hazardous inedibles on green squares send you rushing back to the previous pork sausage red square. Ah, yes! The pork sausages — the winner gets them! Vegetarian version — the loser gets them! If the scoring card is completely covered before the pig in the pantry is reached, then: 1. the nearest player wins; or 2. play the scoring card in reverse by *uncovering* the numbers each turn.

Devised and illustrated by Tony Blundell

1	6	2	9	4
7	3	4	1	6
5	1	10	3	2
2	4	5	1	7
3	8	1	5	0

LOST IN THE WOOD

You need two dice, a counter for each player and a piece of paper and a pencil. Copy this list onto your paper and fill in the last two digits of your own numbers in the blank columns.

Number of letters in first name		
Number of letters in surname		
Your age		
Your birthday		
Number of people in family		

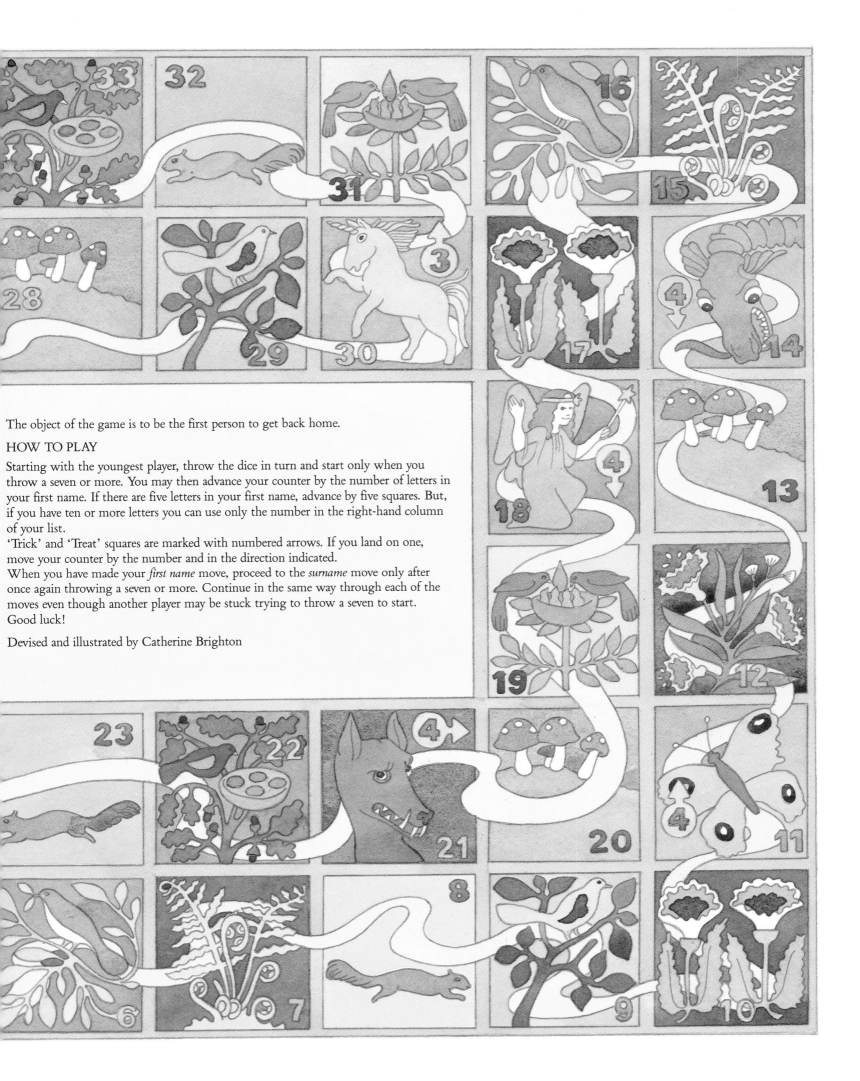

The object of the game is to be the first person to get back home.

HOW TO PLAY

Starting with the youngest player, throw the dice in turn and start only when you throw a seven or more. You may then advance your counter by the number of letters in your first name. If there are five letters in your first name, advance by five squares. But, if you have ten or more letters you can use only the number in the right-hand column of your list.

'Trick' and 'Treat' squares are marked with numbered arrows. If you land on one, move your counter by the number and in the direction indicated.

When you have made your *first name* move, proceed to the *surname* move only after once again throwing a seven or more. Continue in the same way through each of the moves even though another player may be stuck trying to throw a seven to start. Good luck!

Devised and illustrated by Catherine Brighton

HEAVENS ABOVE!

A space race around the planets between the Trumpets and the Grumpets. The first person to reach the finish is the winner. To play this game you need a dice and two counters. You can have an extra turn if you throw a six.

Devised and illustrated by Peter Cross

PICNIC

teddy bears' draughts for two players

This is a special kind of draughts invented by bears on a picnic. Afterwards they ate everything (except the maggotty apples!).

The Rules

1 Each player has five counters. Place two on the first row and three on the second.

2 Always move *diagonally* and only on the food squares.

3 As in draughts, the aim is to take your opponent's counters by jumping over them.

4 If you *can* take a counter, you *must* do so.

5 If you land on a *cake*, you may have an extra move with any one of your counters.

6 If you land on a *maggotty apple*, you lose your counter.

7 As in draughts, once your counter reaches the opposite side of the board, it can move both backwards and forwards. Put one counter on top of another to show that it is a "double decker".

Devised by Susanna Gretz and Alison Sage
Illustrated by Susanna Gretz

I'm **sure** we packed more sandwiches..?

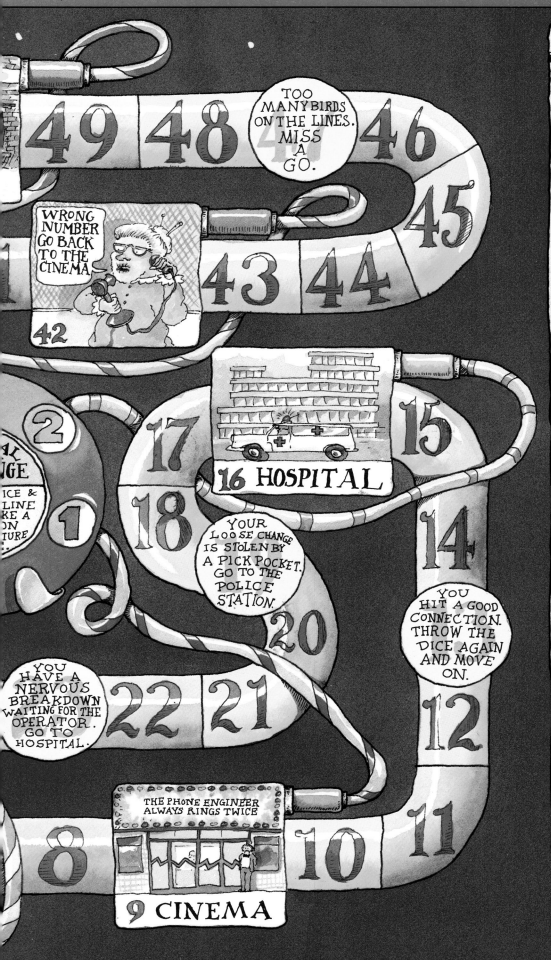

The Phone Game

for two to ★ six players ★

You are trying to phone your mother on the other side of the world. It may be quicker to start digging and visit her!

TO PLAY

You will need a dice, and a counter of a different colour for each player.

Start at square 1 and throw a six to start.

Throw the dice in turn and move your counters by the number thrown.

If you land on a picture square, go to the CENTRAL EXCHANGE (unless you arrived at the picture square from one of the circles). Throw the dice again and move to the picture square which is plugged into the number thrown.

The winner is the first player to connect up with mother by throwing the exact number to land on square 55.

If you throw too high a number to land exactly on 55 move backwards by the excess amount.

Devised and illustrated by Shoo Rayner.

BUM

GAMES

HARES	BEARS
1	1
2	2
3	3
4	4
5	5
6	6

SETS

1	1
2	2
3	3
4	4
5	5

The rules are exactly as used in tennis. As these are rather difficult for the tiniest players, perhaps a grown-up can act as referee and scorer. Young children will then very quickly learn the rules of tennis. Playing BUMBLEDON can make watching Wimbledon on television more interesting, or watching Wimbledon can explain the rules of BUMBLEDON.

OR . . . Clever grown-ups can simplify the rules by not using the second service, and not using Deuce and Advantage.

BUMBLEDON RULES

1 When in doubt, BUMBLEDON is played just like real tennis.
2 You will need one dice; one counter for the ball; and six small items, such as spent matchsticks, for pointers on the scorecards.
3 Scoring is as in tennis. Use the right hand scorecard. There are six games in the set, and five sets in a match. Use the left scorecard to remember games and sets.

Devised and illustrated by Tony Ross

HARES	BEARS
LOVE	LOVE
15	15
30	30
40	40
DEUCE	
ADV.	ADV.
GAME	GAME

TO PLAY

1 Toss a coin to decide who serves. The winner places the ball on one of his players' racquets.

2 Throw dice. Move the ball over the net to the spot corresponding to the number thrown.

3 Should the number be one, then the serve is out (fault), and a second serve is allowed. If one is thrown again, then the serve is out again (double fault), and the point goes to the receiving player.

4 The same player continues to serve until all the points of one game have been decided. The service then passes over the net to the opposing player who serves throughout the next game.

5 Should the dice throw 2, 3, 4, or 5 the ball passes over the net onto the corresponding racquet. The opposing player then throws the dice to return the ball across the net. This is called a rally and can go on for some time. If a 1 is thrown during a rally, ball is out and point goes to the other player.

6 If a six is thrown, the ball is in, has beaten the opponent, and a point is scored by the player who has just thrown the dice.

DON'T DO THAT!

A wicked game devised by Ralph Steadman and Helen Wire.

The problem with you children today is that you are not naughty enough. Here's your chance to be really wicked and still not hurt anybody. If you have ever thought of putting Golden Syrup in dad's overcoat pocket, or a raw egg in his slippers, then this is the game for you and you won't even get into trouble.

Naturally you start off by being boringly good and gradually you become ecstatically horrible — otherwise you won't win — and if you don't win, then the one who does can do something awful to you like put jelly in your sleeping bag or devise a devilish deed for you to do. It's all pretend of course, but just thinking about the sheer naughtiness of it fills you with delight.

The Rules
Any number of aspiring little fiends may play. You will need a counter of a different colour for each player, two dice, paper and pencils.

Starting at the yellow goodie goodie's face, each player throws the dice in turn and moves his/her counter by the number cast. Your object is to **Go To The Devil** with the highest possible score. Keep a running total of the numbers on each circle you *finally* land on. You may only land on the Devil's nose by throwing the exact number to do so. However, once there you are safe, *even from cheats*, and may reward yourself with an extra 500 points. You may cheat once anytime you throw a double five.

Only when you have gone to the Devil may you indulge in the dirty deeds on the Devil's circles (marked with the pips of the dice) and add vast amounts to your score whilst waiting for the other players to finish. Now that you have reached the Devil's playground, use only one dice and each turn move to the circle corresponding to the number cast. However, if

any other player gets to the Devil for the first time and catches you out on a Devil's circle, then you must give them 100 of your points. At any one of your turns now, you can miss a go and stay safely on the Devil's nose or return to the Devil's nose without throwing the dice.

The game ends only when all players have reached the Devil and the one with the highest score wins. The winner may then devise an especially evil deed to be carried out by the player who finishes with the lowest score.

*Royal Society for the Protection of Flies.

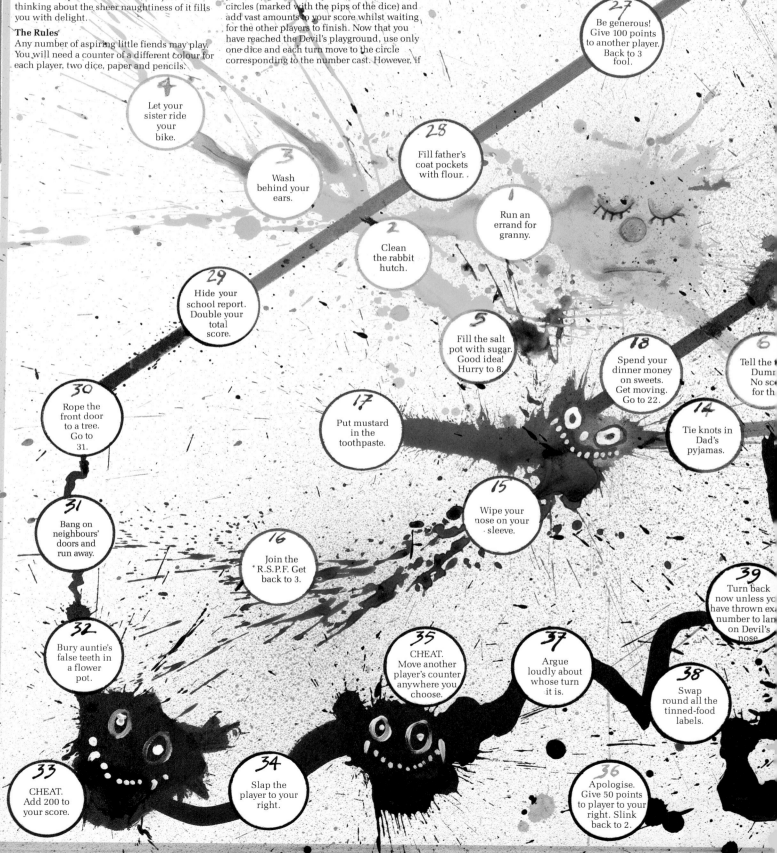

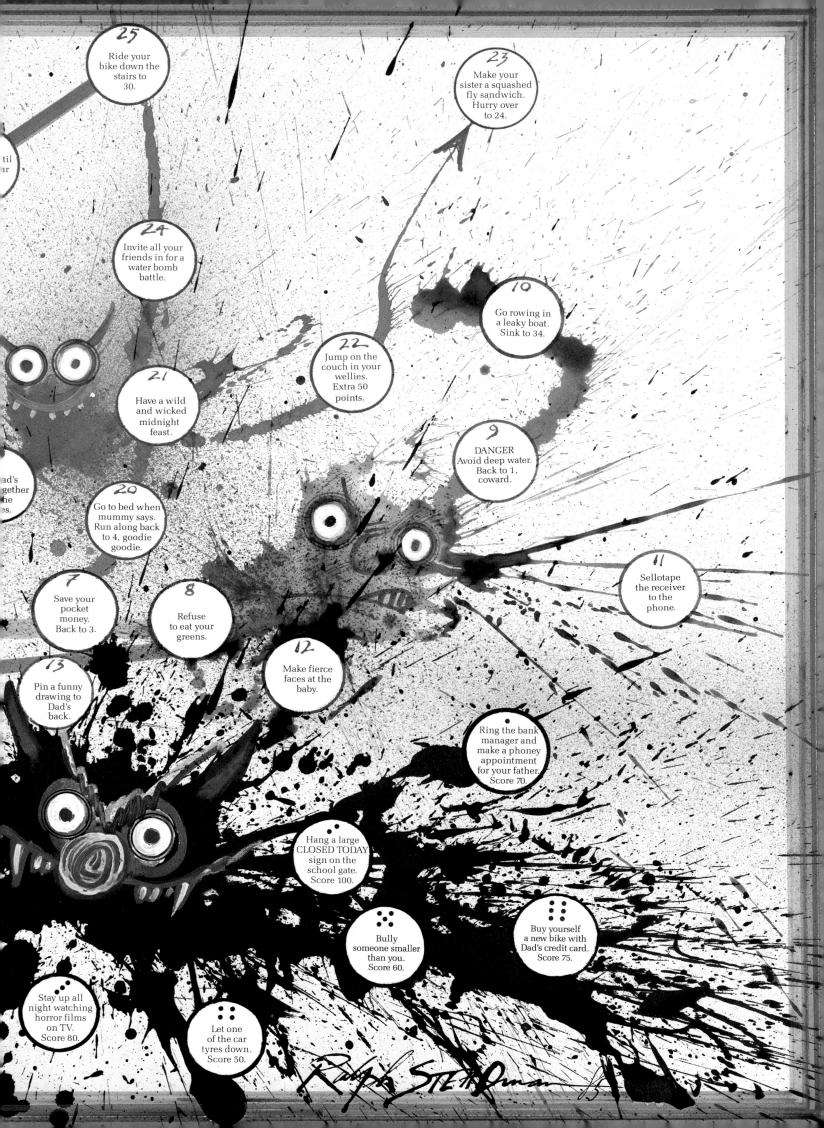

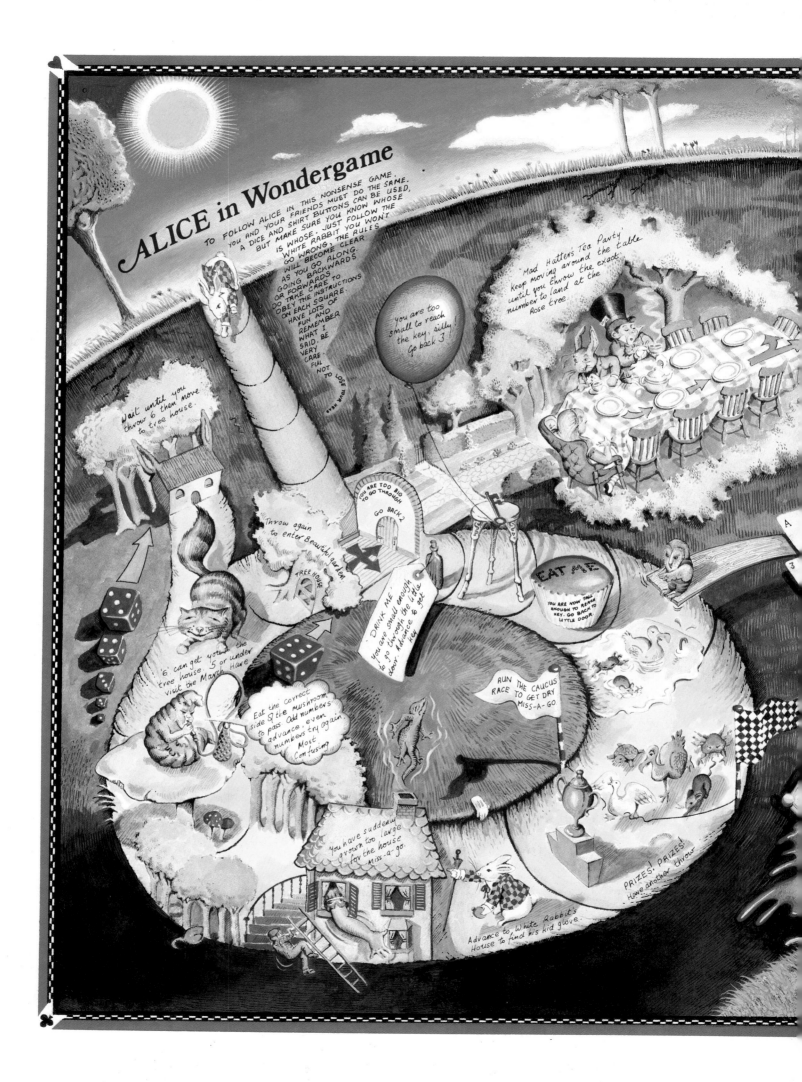

The Game of Goose

Illustrated by Fulvio Testa

A race game for any number of players, based on a traditional Italian board game.

You will need two dice; and a counter of a different colour and twelve tokens for each player. Tokens are used as fines and rewards so decide carefully what you want to use.

The first player to reach 90 wins the game and collects any tokens left in the central pool.

TO PLAY

1. Each player must contribute three tokens to the pool.
2. Draw lots to decide who will start. Then each player throws the dice in turn and advances their counter by the number thrown.
3. If you land on a Goose square you must immediately advance again by the number just thrown. The geese are regularly spaced at nine-square intervals so anyone who throws a nine to start would, by this method, advance straight to 90. To avoid this, if your first throw is a nine made up of a six and a three, go to 26; but if it consists of a five and a four, go to 53.
4. Any player who throws a twelve goes straight to 89 and has a second throw, but with only one dice. If a one is thrown, that player wins the game. If not, the player must move back by twice the number thrown and if he lands on a Goose, he must go back again by the same amount.
5. If another player lands on a square you occupy, you must pay a fine and go to the space your opponent has just left.

of Goose

6. Take a reward from the pool whenever you land on a fruit square (34, 44 or 84).
7. Make the following forfeits whenever you land on:
   The Bridge (6): Pay a fine. Advance to 12.
   The Flag (19): Pay a fine. Miss 2 turns.
   The Well (31): Pay a fine.
   The Castle (42): Pay a fine. Go back to 30.
   The Prison (52): Pay a fine and wait until another player lands on 52. That player will pay a fine to release you to go to the square he/she has just left. The second player must then wait on 52 until he is released in the same way.
   Death's Head (58): Pay a fine. Return to Start.
   The Fountain (71): Return to square you've just left.
   The Tower (82): Pay a fine and, as for the Prison, wait until another player arrives to replace you.
8. To win the game you must throw the exact number to reach 90. If the number thrown takes you past 90, double it and move backwards by that number.

Other beautiful picture books illustrated
by some of the artists in this book

JEZ ALBOROUGH
The Grass is Always Greener (Dial, 1987)
Running Bear (Knopf, 1986)
Bare Bear (Knopf, 1984)

QUENTIN BLAKE
The Story of the Dancing Frog (Knopf, 1985)
Quentin Blake's Nursery Rhyme Book (Harper & Row, 1984)

TONY BLUNDELL
Boomps-a-Daisy: Forty Singable Songs (Sterling, 1986)
Joe on Sunday (Dial, 1987)

CATHERINE BRIGHTON
Five Secrets in a Box (Dutton, 1987)
The Picture (Faber & Faber, 1986)

PETER CROSS
Trouble for Trumpets (Random House, 1985)

SUSANNA GRETZ
Roger Takes Charge! (Dial, 1987)
Teddy Bears ABC (Macmillan, 1986)
Too Dark! (Macmillan, 1986)

SATOSHI KITAMURA
When Sheep Cannot Sleep (Farrar, Straus & Giroux, 1986)
What's Inside? The Alphabet Book
(Farrar, Straus & Giroux, 1985)

TONY ROSS
Stone Soup (Dial, 1987)
Foxy Fables (Dial, 1986)

RALPH STEADMAN
That's My Dad (David & Charles, 1987)

FULVIO TESTA
Wolf's Favor (Dial, 1986)
If You Look Around You (Dial, 1983)